To my supporting family and friends, I dedicate this book to you all for your unwavering encouragement and confidence in me: Gloria, Camita, Tracelyn, Loretta, Marshall, Keyana, Shyla, Mary, Linda, Sonzie, Peggy, Kimberly, Bonita, Patsy, Jesse, Candice, Harmony, Keyon, Zay and Jerome.

Thank you for your love, patience, and understanding: Aaron, Robert, Gary Jr., and Hannah JaQueen.

Ordering Information:
For details, contact- vickiannbonner@gmail.com
Print ISBN: 978-0-578-87277-3
eBook ISBN: 978-057-887276-6

Goodnight Blue

Written By Vicki Ann Bonner
Pictures By Travis A. Thompson

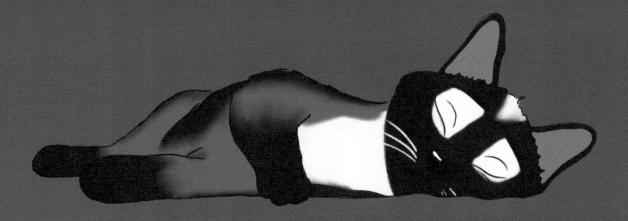

In a city, in a house, down the street lives a cat named "Blue."

He likes to play with people's feet; it's his favorite thing to do.

Blue enjoys running fast

We adopted Blue from a shelter in his distant past.

Blue loves to run, jump, and play.

While he has laid in the sun for the day.

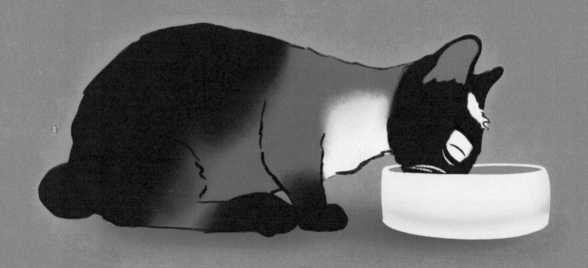

Blue goes to his bowl to eat.

He's a quick eater who also loves treats.

The sun is setting and
Blue yawns widely.

To show his little teeth
for all to see.

It has been a good, fun, and exciting day.

Blue heads over to his comfy place to lay.

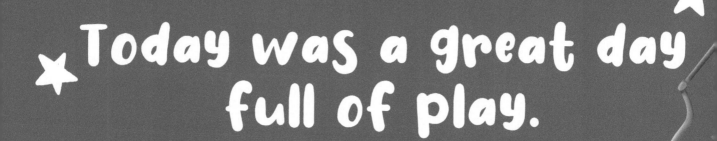

Today was a great day full of play.

The sun has finally gone away.

So, Blue curls up into a ball really tight.

He nods his head to say
"Goodnight."

Vicki Ann Bonner was born and raised in Georgia, and grew up in foster care. She received her degree in Business Administration and Computer Information Technology at Gwinnett College of Lilburn, Georgia. She began writing her first children's picture book during the pandemic of 2020. Her love of writing began at an early age, while obsessing over her favorite authors, Zerna Sharp and William S. Gray, book series about "Dick and Jane" for basal readers, in the early 1970's. When not writing, she can be found traveling or journaling. Vicki currently lives in Atlanta with her son, daughters, chihuahua terrier mix named, Bentley, and "Blue" the Siamese Cat.

CPSIA information can be obtained
at www.ICGtesting.com
Printed in the USA
BVHW020244120521
607039BV00002B/60